All About Me

By Catherine Bruzzone
and Lone Morton
Illustrated by Caroline Jayne Church

b small publishing
www.bsmall.co.uk

More about me

The following pages are for you to fill in lots of details about yourself, your family, your friends, your school and your pastimes. You may collect more information, photos or souvenirs than you have room for in this book, so here are some ideas for keeping everything together.

You can clip extra paper to the pages, like this:

Or you can make a special envelope on the inside of the back cover, like this:

Cut a triangle from card. Glue or tape it to the back cover.

Or you can make a separate book, like this:

Punch holes in the extra paper. Thread through pieces of wool to hold them together.

To keep your book and extra paper together, tie a ribbon round them, like this:

Now you can read it again when you're older – or even show it to your own children!

Published by b small publishing ltd
The Book Shed, 36 Leyborne Park, Kew, Richmond, Surrey, TW9 3HA, UK
www.bsmall.co.uk

Text and illustrations © b small publishing, 1992
This edition first published 2006

5   4

Printed in China by WKT Co. Ltd.

British Library Cataloguing-in-Publication Data.
A record of this book is available from the British Library.

ISBN-10: 1-905710-16-X
ISBN-13: 978-1-905710-16-4

Self-portrait

Look in the mirror to help you draw a picture of yourself here.

Me, age ....
Date I drew this picture ....

Have you ever seen a portrait in a museum or art gallery? Was the person standing or sitting? Could you only see their head and shoulders? Did they wear special clothes?

Me

My name is

My birthday

Where I was born

Year I was born

Weight when I was born

Time I was born

Length when I was born

STICK IN PHOTOGRAPH

Photo of me as a baby, age ....

Nationality

Languages I can speak

_____

Colour of eyes

_____

Colour of hair

_____

My thumb print

This is a lock of my hair

Practise this on a separate piece of paper before you start. Paint your thumb with a bright colour. Let it dry slightly. Then press it firmly on the paper and roll it carefully from side to side without lifting it up.

Ask an adult to help you cut a small lock of hair

Age I am now, date

_____

Height I am now

_____

Weight I am now

_____

My hand span

Why not make a hand print and a foot print too? Do them on separate sheets of paper and clip them to this page or start an extra book. Look at the suggestions for this on page 2.

5

Musical instruments I am learning

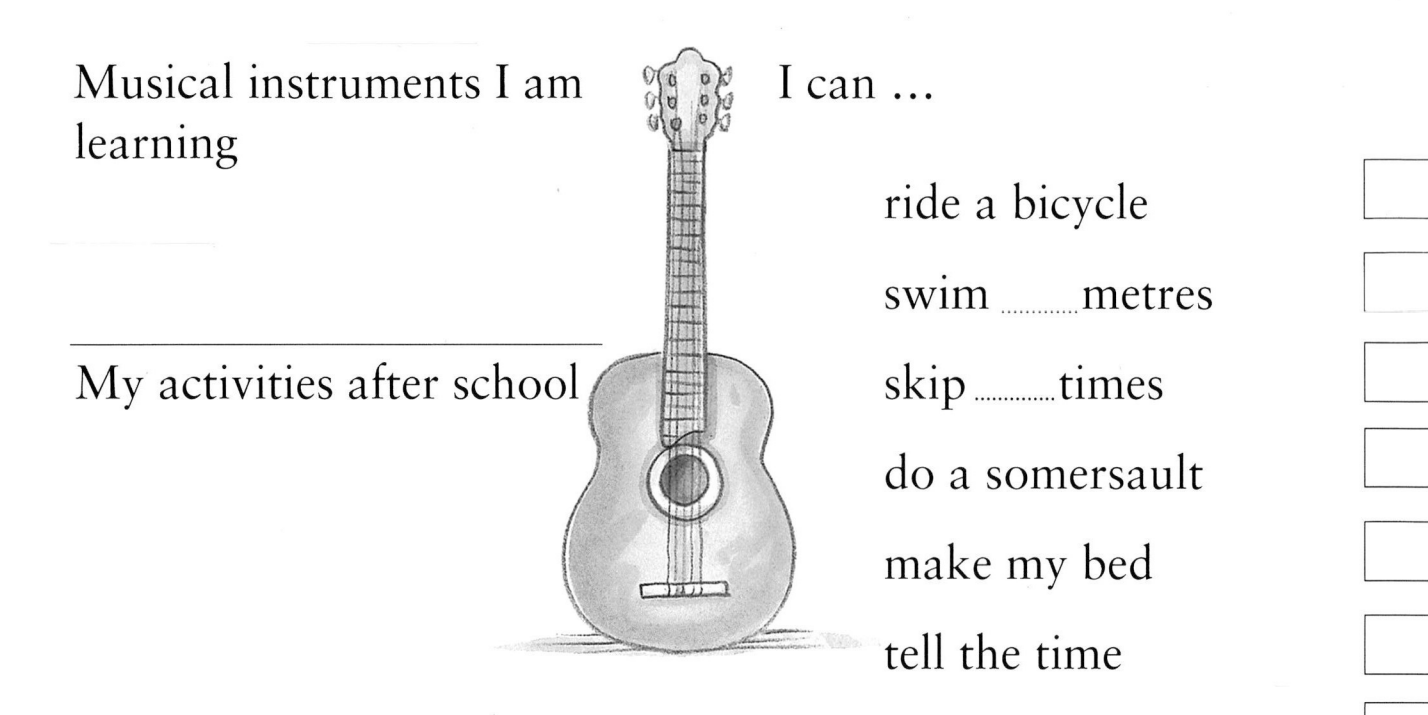

_____

My activities after school

I can …

ride a bicycle ☐

swim .... metres ☐

skip .... times ☐

do a somersault ☐

make my bed ☐

tell the time ☐

tie my shoelaces ☐

I can …

List any other things you can do.

Don't forget any activities you do at the weekend.

_____

How high I can jump

_____

How far I can jump

_____

6

My worst habit

_____

What makes me sad

What makes me happy

_____

My signature

I'm really good at

1
_____
2
_____
3
_____
4
_____
5
_____
6
_____
7
_____
8
_____
9
_____
10
_____

The best thing about me

_____

My family

My mother's name is

_____

Surname when she was born

_____

Date she was born

_____

My father's name is

_____

Date he was born

_____

Name of person who looks after me

_____

Date he or she was born

_____

Number of sisters

Number of brothers

My oldest sister's or brother's name is

age

_____

My next oldest sister's or brother's name is

age

_____

My next oldest sister's or brother's name is

age

_____

If you have a large family, you will probably need an extra sheet of paper. You can write the names of aunts, uncles and cousins too.
Do you also have a step-family or half-sisters and brothers? You could describe them too: 'John is my stepfather. His children's names are George, Lucy and Toby. They are my stepbrothers and sisters'.
'Jason is my half-brother. John and my mother are his parents'.

STICK IN PHOTOGRAPH

Write the names of the people in the photo. When was it taken?

My grandparents' names – my
mother's parents

My grandparents' names – my
father's parents

Can you draw a family tree? Ask someone to help you. Perhaps someone in your family has already drawn one?

Where I live

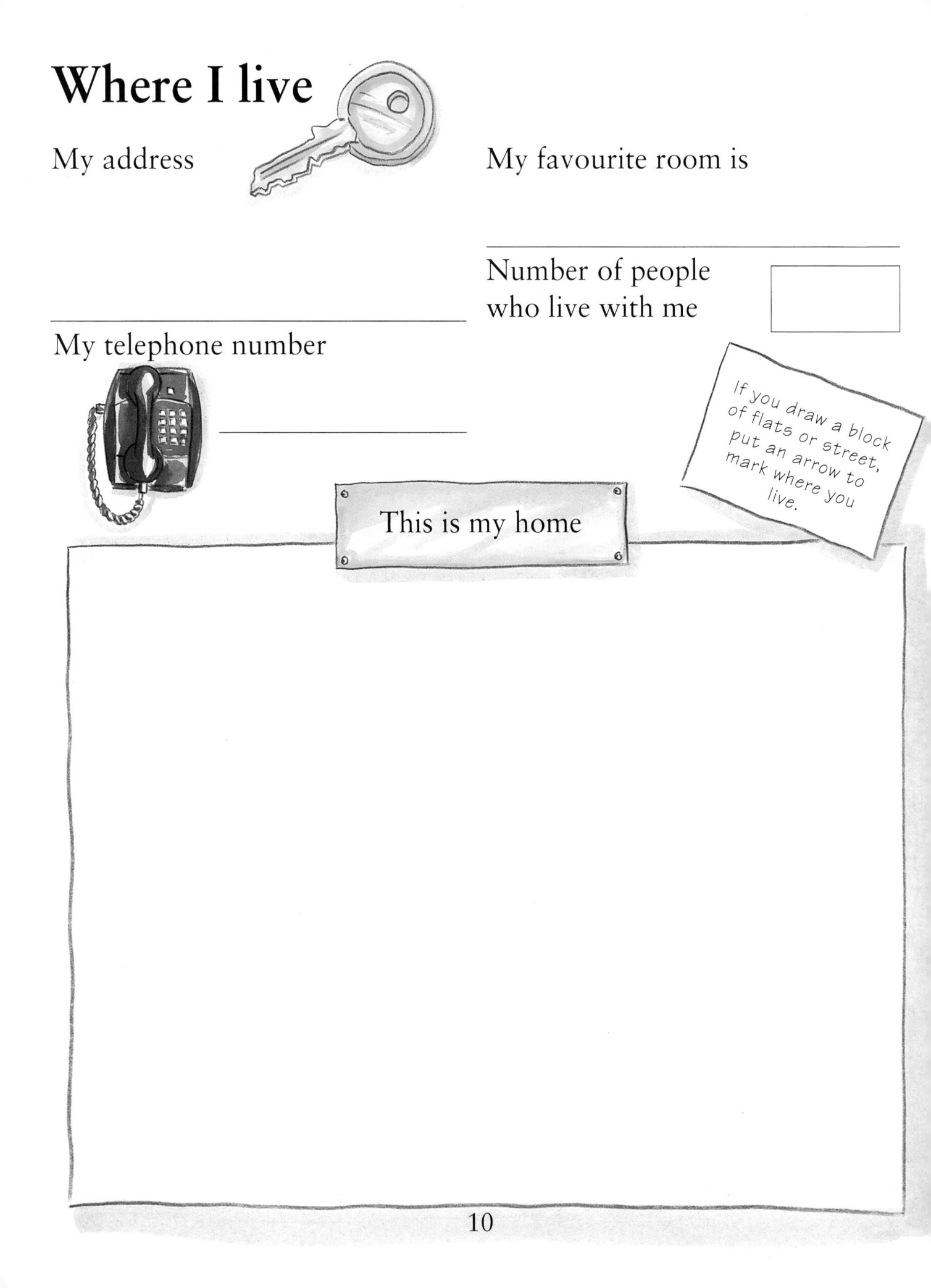

My address

My telephone number

My favourite room is

Number of people
who live with me

If you draw a block
of flats or street,
put an arrow to
mark where you
live.

This is my home

The neighbourhood where I live is ...

My neighbourhood in the past

Can you find an old postcard or photo showing your neighbourhood in the past? Can you ask your grandparents or neighbours about it?

Describe the area where you live. Is it a big city or a small town? Is it a village or the middle of the country? Is it in the mountains or near the sea?

The worst thing about where I live is

The most special thing about where I live is

Names of my nearest neighbours

Map of my neighbourhood

You may need help with this. You can mark your home, your nearest shop, your school, the nearest bus stop or railway station.

My school

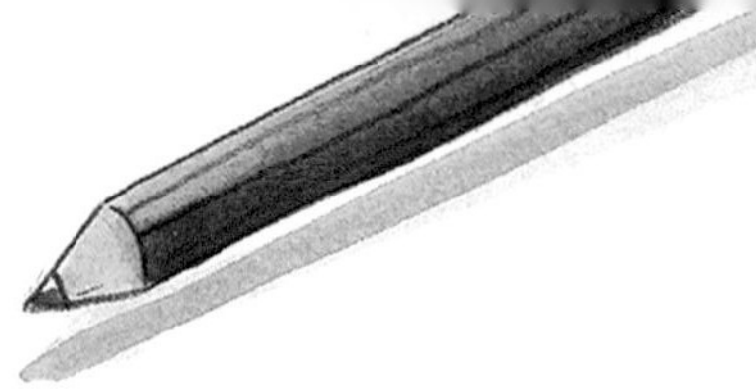

Name of my school

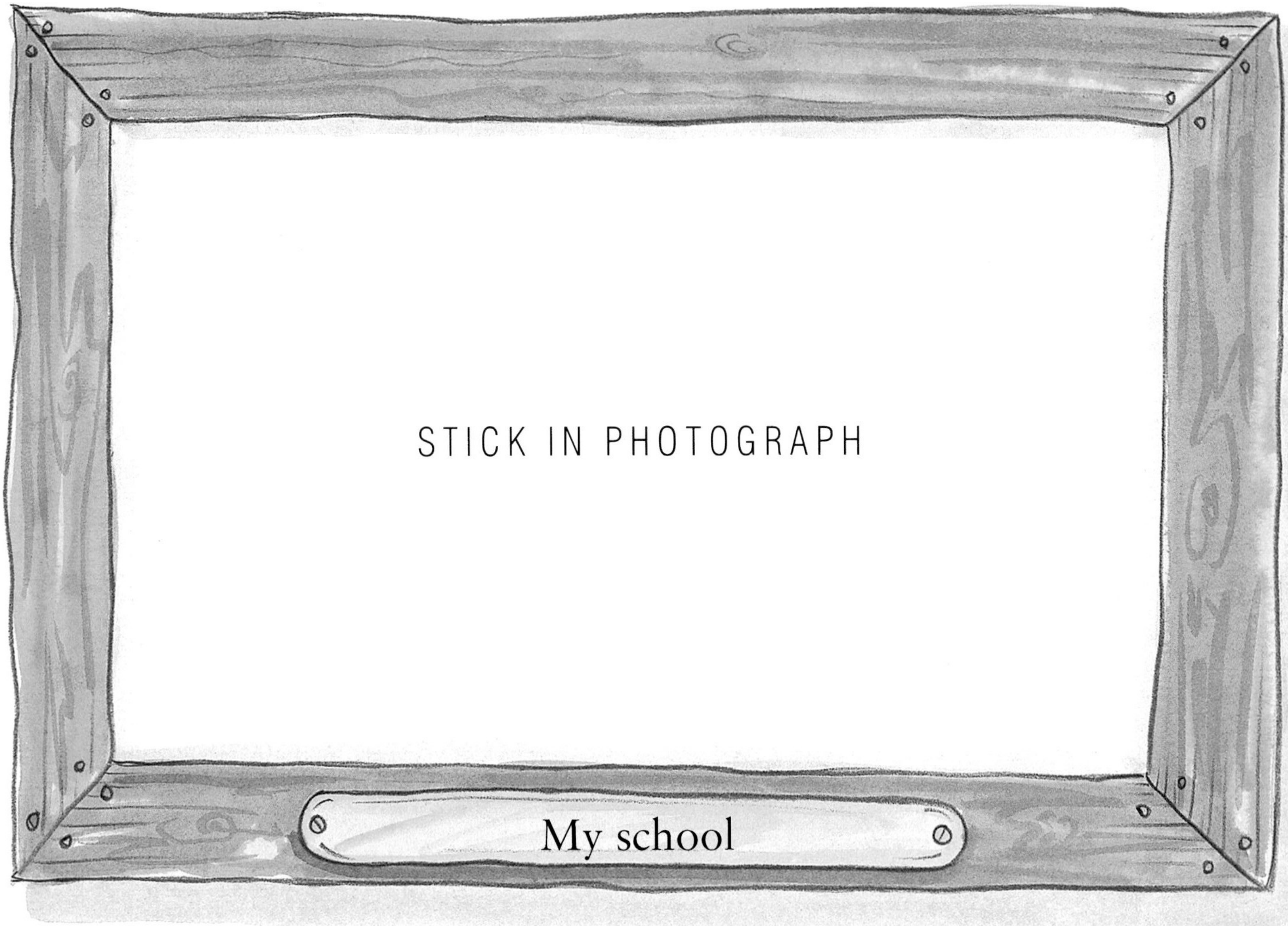
STICK IN PHOTOGRAPH
My school

Address

Telephone number

Head teacher's name

6+
2
8

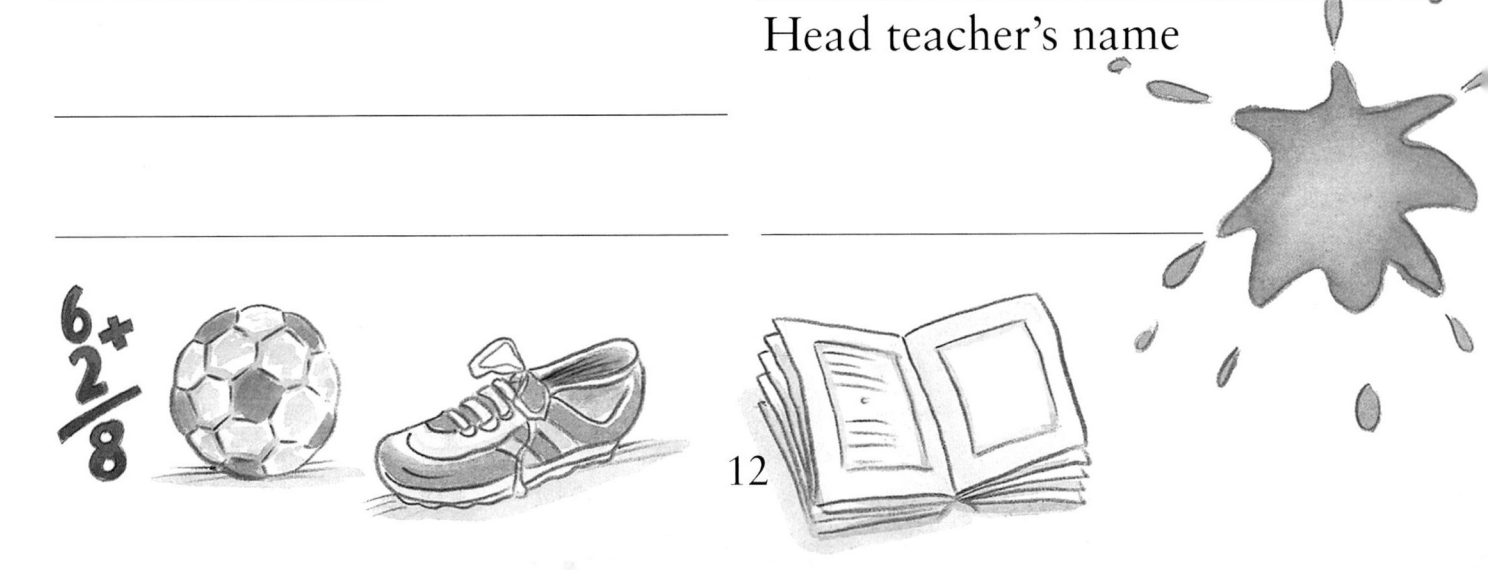

Number of children
in my school

Names of my school friends

Name or number of my class

_____

_____

My teacher's name

_____

_____

Names of the children I sit next
to in class

_____

_____

Draw your teacher here.

I start school at .... o'clock

Number of children
in my class

I finish school at .... o'clock

Number of girls

Number of boys

START   FINISH

Days of the week I go to school

Sports I do at school

My favourite lesson

My worst lesson

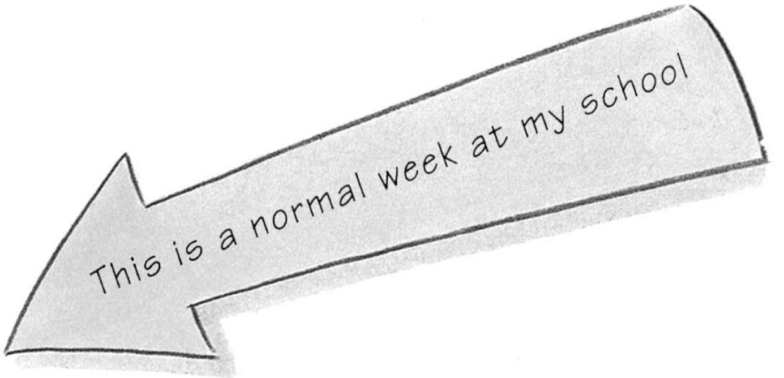

This is a normal week at my school

Monday	Tuesday	Wednesday	Thursday	Friday	Saturday
		Lunch break			

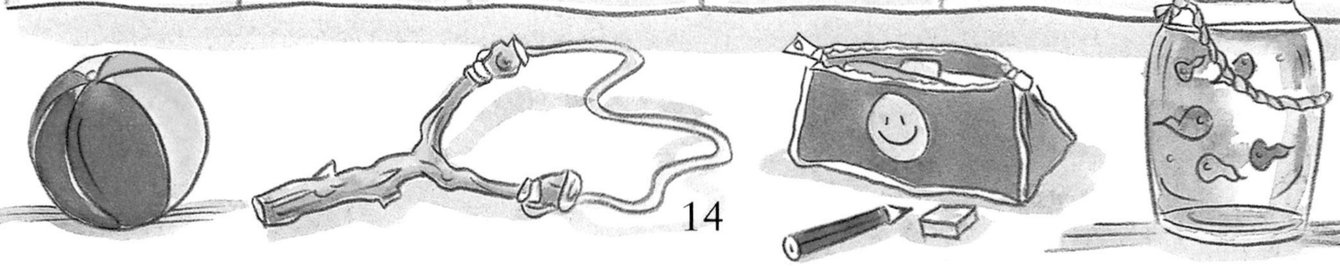

My favourite lunch at school

If you have a packed lunch, you can still draw it on the plate.

My favourite school joke

What I do in the playground

Do you know any skipping games or playground rhymes? Write them on a piece of paper and clip them to this page.

My favourite school outing

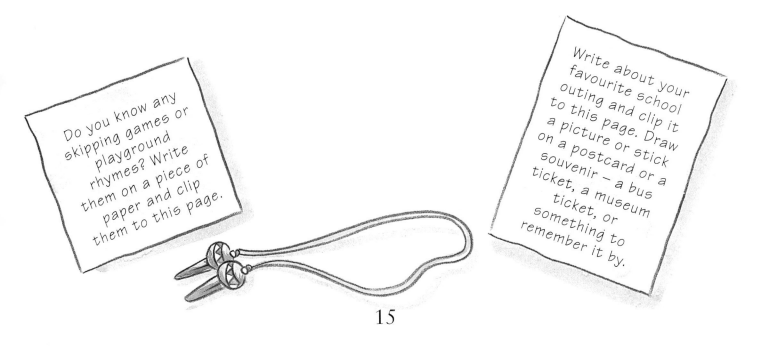

Write about your favourite school outing and clip it to this page. Draw a picture or stick on a postcard or a souvenir – a bus ticket, a museum ticket, or something to remember it by.

My friends

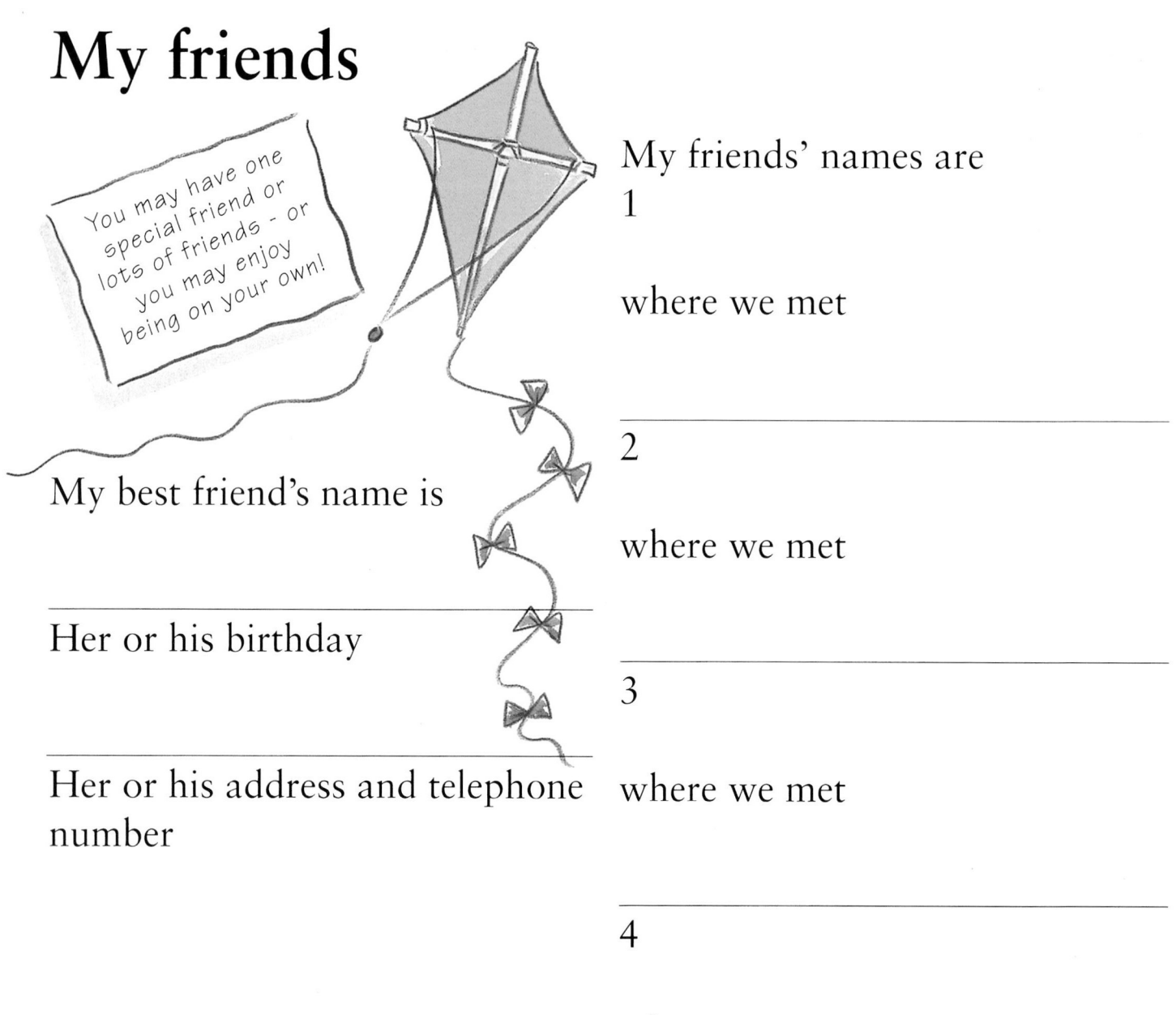

You may have one special friend or lots of friends - or you may enjoy being on your own!

My best friend's name is

_____

Her or his birthday

_____

Her or his address and telephone number

_____

My friends' names are

1

where we met

_____

2

where we met

_____

3

where we met

_____

4

where we met

5

where we met

_____

6

where we met

_____

7

where we met

_____

Write a poem about a friend – it could be a real friend or an imaginary friend

Draw your friends' portraits here

Design badges for your friends

You could make these badges. Cut out circles from stiff card. Tape a safety pin on the back.

My likes and dislikes

My favourite colour

_____

My least favourite colour

_____

My favourite book or author

_____

A book I didn't enjoy

_____

My favourite TV programme

_____

My worst TV programme

_____

My favourite sport

_____

This is my favourite food

This is the food I hate!

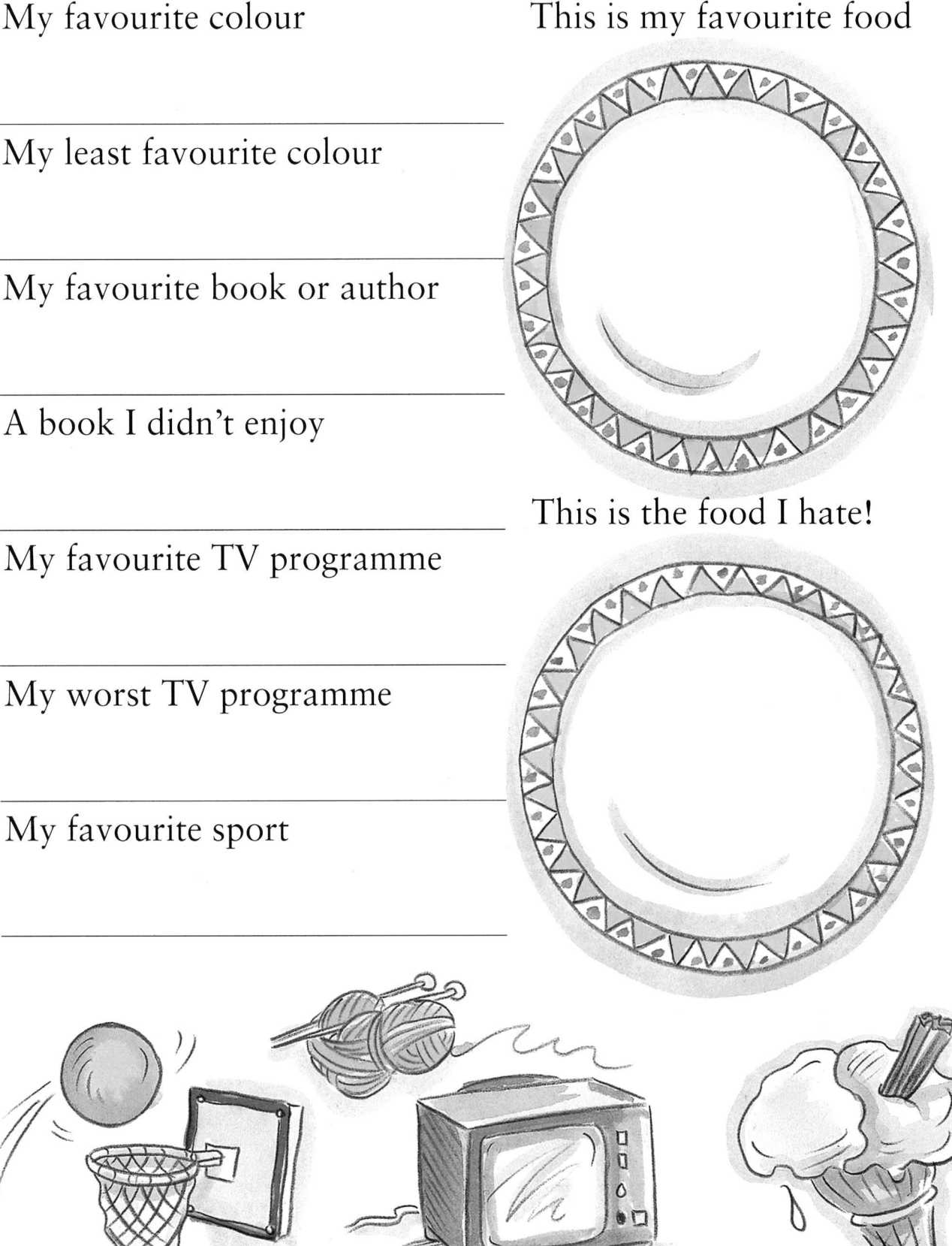

My favourite film

A film which frightened me

My best cartoon character

My favourite pop star

My favourite record

My favourite time of year

What I want for my next birthday

The worst day in my life was ...

The best day in my life was ...

What I hate doing most in the world!

What I enjoy doing best in the world!

My clothes

What I like wearing best

_____

What I hate wearing

_____

What I wear at night

_____

What I wear to school

_____

My favourite shoes

_____

My dream fancy-dress costume

Design-a-t-shirt

You could try your design on a real t-shirt. Look for special fabric paints and plain t-shirts in the shops.

Draw your dream costume here. Can you stick on little samples of material? Colour and label your costume.

My pets

My favourite pet

My pet's name

My pet's age

When I bought or was given my pet

My other pets

A pet I would like to have

Looking after my pet

If you don't have a pet, you could write about a pet you would like to own.

List the important things you need to do to care for your pet.

My pet's food

Where my pet sleeps

The best thing about my pet

STICK IN PHOTOGRAPH

my pet

Does your pet also live in the wild? Which country does it come from? Is it a hot or cold country? Can you find that country on a map?

My country

Name of my country

_____

Capital city

_____

Main language spoken

_____

This is my country's flag

Highest mountain

_____

Longest river

_____

Can you mark where you live on the map?

This is a map of my country

My holidays

Time I get up in the holidays

_____

Time I go to bed

_____

My favourite holiday activity

_____

What I don't like about holidays

_____

Where I went on my last holiday

_____

Where I am going on my next holiday

_____

Collect a souvenir from a place you visited in the holidays – a postcard, bus ticket, stamp, ticket for a museum, or sugar wrapper.

My best holiday

_____

Write a postcard to your teacher from your dream holiday. Or draw a picture.

Me in the future

My age next birthday

_____

What I want to do for my next
birthday party

_____

My next school

_____

An activity or sport I want to try

_____

An activity or sport I want to
give up

_____

My New Year's resolutions
1

_____

2

_____

3

_____

What I want to do when I grow
up

_____

A wish for the future

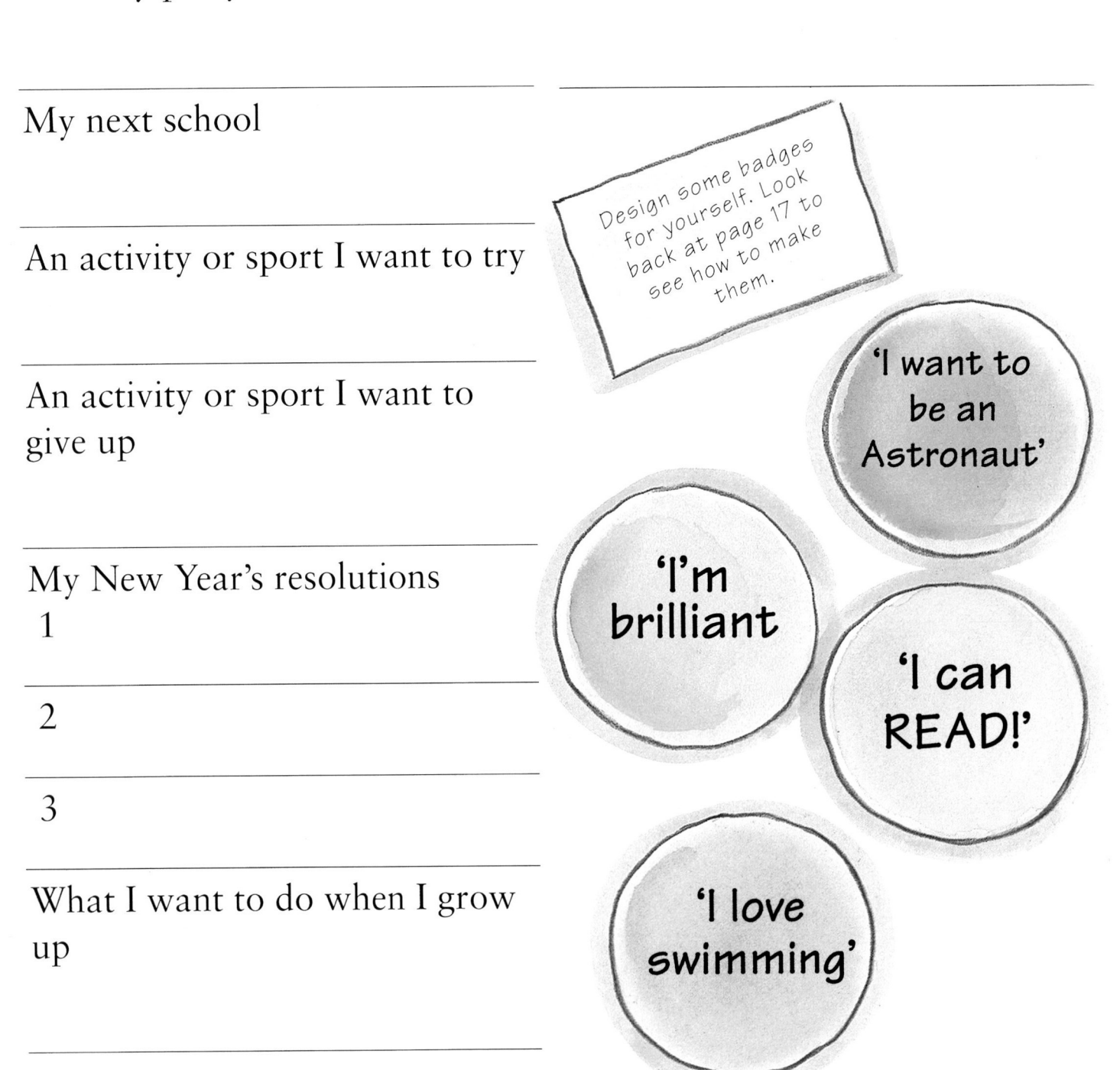

Design some badges
for yourself. Look
back at page 17 to
see how to make
them.

'I want to
be an
Astronaut'

'I'm
brilliant

'I can
READ!'

'I love
swimming'